And he took the children in his arms,
placed his hands on them
and blessed them.

Mark 10:16

About the art

The collage artwork presented in *The Perfect Gift* was created by nine precious preschool children. The midnight blue pages with a hint of silver glitter were done rolling the paint with a brayer. Sheets of gold, brown, and yellow with a tint of brown paint were used to bring life to the stars, the stable and the straw. This is why no two pages or characters are the same. The uniqueness of this Christmas book can be attributed to the purity and innocence of the children's drawings such as the angel, with the long beautiful eyelashes!

Scripture taken from the Holy Bible, New International Version®, NIV® Copyright © 1973, 1978, 1984, 2011 by Biblica, Inc.®
Used by permission. All rights reserved worldwide.

ISBN 978-0-578-70159-2
Library of Congress Control Number: 2020913059

To the Potter Family.
Blessings,
Karen Dominik

From: GiGi + PopPop
2020

The Perfect Gift

by Karen Dominik

Mary rode
on a donkey.

Mary and Joseph
went to Bethlehem.

There was no room
in the inn.

They stayed in a stable.

A star shone brightly that night,
telling everyone that
Jesus was born!

Mary laid Jesus
in a manger.

A beautiful angel told the shepherds
about a new baby born
in Bethlehem.

Three kings followed
the shooting star
to the stable.

They brought Baby Jesus special gifts
for the King of all Kings.

This is the story
of the very first Christmas.
Jesus is our perfect gift
from God.

Thanks be to God
for his indescribable gift!

2 Corinthians 9:15

Acknowledgements

First and foremost, I thank God for putting insightful people in my path, including my family and friends, who, through their help and encouragement, took *The Perfect Gift* all the way to production. I owe a debt of gratitude and heartfelt thanks to Wonder Years Preschool of First Presbyterian Church in Bonita Springs, Florida, for allowing me to create this special book!

About the Author

Karen Dominik was born in Neville Island located on the Ohio River, west of Pittsburgh, PA. She holds a BS in Elementary Education with an emphasis in early childhood. She taught kindergarten, first grade and preschoolers for 25 years. She currently resides in Southwest Florida, is an avid tennis player and enjoys the game of Bridge. Karen's faith journey began in 1998 while touring with the Continental Singers, an international music ministry based out of California. She sings in a choir, contemporary church group and a community chorus. Karen's highlight during the school year is volunteering at her church's preschool. Creating books and involving children in the process, has always been a passion of hers, with *The Perfect Gift* being Karen's first published book.